Mike Was Here

Connie Moore Hunt

BROADMAN PRESS
Nashville, Tennessee

Library of Congress Catalog Card Number: 81-68368
Dewey Decimal Classification: F
Subject heading: PARENT AND CHILD-FICTION
Printed in the United States of America

This story of a child
comes with gratitude
to
Beth and John
Ann and Bill
Anne and Steve
who because of their superb parenting
and their generous affection as adult children
have caused grandparenthood to be
not the anticipated old-age image
but a surprising land of love and renewal

Contents

Before

Mike is the most beautiful four-year-old on this present earth. Just ask his grandmother, she will tell you.

Others would say the same about his beauty. Mike has fair skin, and his large, dark eyes are shadowed by long thick lashes. He has a way of looking out of them, with his head very straight and still, that utterly bewitches. His hair is thick, dark, and very soft; it would not dare to curl. His cheeks are round and pudgy enough to proclaim his four-year-old status, and they are tinged the color of his grandfather's—ruddy.

Mike's name is perfect for him. He is masculine to the core, preordained to be a lord of creation. He stands firm on short, stocky legs. His feet are in tennis shoes that are forever worn out, and his long pants slip down over his fat little tummy.

Mike's vocabulary is extensive and his pronunciation almost flawless. His *v*'s tend to become *b*'s so that something "very good" is "bery good." The intent is obvious, however, and the *b*'s are ignored except for a warm feeling in the hearts of his hearers. He gestures with his hands as he talks, especially with a pointed forefinger. He speaks always with authority when he is giving advice or consent. When he is teasing, he openly avows it by a playful tone of voice, "Hello, *precious*," and a chuckle.

Mike is a gentleman. He is kind and polite to toddlers, ladies, and others in need of his attention. If provoked, he is quick to flare. He can roar, and he has been known to bite when the victim was older and bigger than he could handle otherwise. But his father has given him reasons to change such tactics. Mike is not so unwise as to be fearless but has astounding wit about what is worth the price and what is not.

Above all, Mike is valiant. Even if the cost is staggering, and he knows he must pay it to the full limit, he will take a deep breath and fight the right against the wrong. "That's not FAIR!" he will cry against what seems to him an unjust decision. With trembling lips, he will take banishment to his own room, staying until grownups long for his return. When he reappears with a dazzling smile making rainbows of his tearful cheeks, his adversaries dissolve and vie for his favor, which he bestows unstintingly.

When rodeo time came in Fort Worth, Mike's vivacious Auntie Gin was not about to let it go unnoticed by the rest of the family. She got tickets for everyone who could come. Mike and his brother, Bill, a seven-year-old, came with their parents to join the fun with Auntie Gin and their grandfather and grandmother. Their two-year-old cousin, Wesley, and his parents couldn't come. They lived too far away.

No one could resist Auntie Gin's plans. Mike and Bill followed her from barn to barn, viewing cattle and sheep and pigs on the way to the arena where brave cowboys rode bucking broncs and wrestled Brahma bulls. "Right on!" cheered Auntie Gin.

"Right on!" responded Mike between mouths of popcorn, cotton candy, soft drinks, and more popcorn.

The next afternoon, while his parents packed the car for their return home, Grandmother found Mike sitting by himself. His arms folded across his chest, Mike was pouting belligerently and mumbling terrifying threats to everybody in the world—most particularly his mommy and daddy.

"They TOLD me," he said with a sob, "they told me I could stay here for TEN days—ten WHOLE days. Now I have to go home. They didn't tell the truth."

Ah, thought Grandmother, *take your rubies and diamonds, but leave the healing balm of a grandchild who wants to stay with me—even for the moment!* She picked him up, although he was almost too much for that now, carried him into the kitchen, and sat him beside the telephone so that he could see the calendar. "You are going to stay here for ten days," she said firmly, "but the ten days begin next week. See, here on the calendar. . . ." Grandmother counted off the days for Mike and showed him the day she would meet him and his mommy in Waco. Mike would stay in Fort Worth while his parents went to Miami to attend a convention. Mike's world righted itself immediately. He struggled down from the telephone niche, ran to his mommy, and explained the situation, with great authority.

Grandmother had not been willing, at first, to keep one of her adored grandchildren for ten days. Since her children had grown to adulthood and left home, she had begun teaching piano and was enough bound to that schedule to preclude another assignment. Besides, she felt no obligation to babysit for her young adults. They were able to meet such needs. Or so she thought until Mike's mommy reminded her, "Grandmother stayed with us while you went to conventions with Daddy."

"But your sweet grandmother and Mike's grandmother are two different people. I have a different life-style—which you, especially, have encouraged me to have." Mike's grandmother spoke the truth, but memories of those past conventions got to her. She knew how much it would mean to her daughter and son-in-law to be away together. She remembered the amazing dividends that had come to her in mysterious ways from such times. She most vividly remembered that she could not have had them except that her mother—wise, intelligent, strict, and loving—had relieved her of any worry about the children.

Another thing caused Grandmother to wince, as she anticipated her chubby, adorable visitor. She knew, that after ten days of him, she would be hopelessly hooked. In ten days, he would appropriate her as surely as *le petit prince* tamed his fox. When Mike left, Grandmother would remember him with the same emotion as the fox felt when he saw the golden color of wheat. *Mike will have been here,* she warned herself.

The First Day—Friday

The weatherman reported the incredible fact that it was snowing in South Texas. The highways were icy, and travelers were advised not to. Grandmother was not surprised when Mike's mommy called. "Well, Mama," she said in a brave, sweet, honestly-facing-the-facts voice that moved her mother more than she could dream, "the best laid plans, you know. It's just terrible here, and I could never ask you to come."

How joyous it was to tell her that the roads to Waco were open and dry, only her part of the trip would be difficult. "I'll be there at ten-thirty if you can make it."

"Oh, Mama," her voice lilted, "I can make it!"

They had decided to meet at the university, and Mike and his mommy were waiting when Grandmother arrived. Mike saw Grandmother coming and ran to greet her. He slipped on the shining floor and quickly glanced up to see if Grandmother noticed his ignominious position. She seemed to be trying to find something in her purse. He picked himself up and, more cautiously this time, ran into her arms. Then he went back to his mommy and sort of leaned into her coat.

Toys, suitcases, and clothes on hangers were changed from one car to the other. Mike carefully carried a paper sack, from which an educational boy doll, Dapper Dan, stuck out his head. Dapper Dan had buttons to button, zippers to zip,

shoes to tie, and a very friendly face. Mike took him from the
sack and placed him on the front seat beside Grandmother.
"He likes it up here," said Mike.

Grandmother and Mike hugged and kissed Mike's
mommy good-bye. They told her to be careful and to have a
good time. They told her that they would be careful, that they
would have a good time, and that they would see her in ten
days. They waved and smiled as their car went up the ramp of
the interstate, and her car disappeared under the bridge to go
the opposite direction. Dapper Dan waved too.

Mike was rather quiet as they sped along the highway
toward Fort Worth. He did not welcome any comforting
words or hugs, but he was most pleased when Grandmother
patted Dapper Dan. "Dapper Dan likes to sit by you," he said.
He patted Dapper Dan too. Obviously, Dapper Dan was a bit
insecure. The car was a quiet place.

About halfway home, Grandmother said the magic
words. "I have a surprise."

"A SURPRISE, Grandmother?" His brown eyes came
alive, his body squirmed in delight.

"It is right here in this sack." She lifted a small paper sack
from her side of the car and handed it to him. "We are going to
have a picnic in the car!"

"Can I do it, Grandmother? Can I do it by myself?" He
opened the sack quickly.

"You will have to do it for me, if you will be so kind," she
said solemnly. "I must always keep my eyes on the road when I
drive."

He closed the sack and relaxed with a fond sigh. "I will be
glad to, my dear," he said. He glanced sidewise at her to see if
she were laughing at his endearing terminology, but her eyes
were on the road as she concentrated on her driving.

Grandmother relaxed too. Mike had made it through the initial separation from his family. He was now in command of the situation. He handed her a napkin and spread one out for himself. He poked into the sack and pulled out a small plastic packet.

"Gumdrops!"

"For dessert," she said. "After our sandwiches."

"Three for me and three for you," said Mike, still looking at the gumdrops.

"Actually, I am on a diet, Mike. Those are all for you."

He sucked in his breath. Such magnanimity on her part must not go unrewarded. "I will save one for Grandfather," he said.

Grandfather was tremendously impressed with the saved gumdrop. It was presented to him at the moment of arrival. To Mike's utter satisfaction, Grandfather ate it immediately, licking his lips. "Best gumdrop I ever tasted," he declared. "Thank you for saving it for me, Mike."

Mike glowed. "You are bery welcome, Grandfather." No "precious" or "my dear" would fit this situation.

Grandfather carried suitcases and toys into the blue and antique-white bedroom which had once been Mike's mommy's. Drawers were filled, clothes on hangers were put in the closet, pajamas were looped over a special low hook, ready for evening.

Inside one opened suitcase were gifts, lovingly placed there by a wise mommy, for Mike to give to Grandfather and Grandmother. He bestowed them with ceremony: lipstick for Grandmother, "because it is peach color like you want," and a new hammer for Grandfather's tool closet in the garage.

This called for an immediate trip by the men to the garage. Grandfather carried his new hammer, and Mike carried his own small tool kit, which had been brought for just such a time as this. During a pleasant quarter-hour, plans were laid for the days ahead, plans which only Grandfather and Mike held in trust.

Grandfather left for duties elsewhere. It was nap time for Mike. Naps were a part of Mike's daily routine, and both Mike and Grandmother knew it must be so. At any rate, Grandmother knew. Mike, with the unconscious urge of the human spirit, had to be sure there might not be a better way. But Grandmother, knowing that of the ten days to come, this was the one to establish polity, sternly insisted that what should be would be.

Dapper Dan understood. He was already half asleep on the bed beside Mike. Mike turned Dapper Dan over on his tummy. "He likes to sleep that way," said Mike.

Grandmother patted Dapper Dan. Mike sighed, turned slightly toward Dapper Dan, and closed his eyes. With some restraint, Grandmother merely patted her napping grandchild.

For dinner there was shrimp. Mike and Grandfather heartily approved. Mike, standing on a stool, helped drop the frozen morsels into the boiling, herb-scented water.

Grandfather brought the big dictionary for Mike to sit on at the table. This was as acceptable to Mike as a highchair was not. Mike helped set the table, folding paper napkins into the most marvelous shapes. The centerpiece was an arrangement of pink, red, and lavender silk flowers, in anticipation of Valentine's Day on Wednesday of next week. Mike had a lifetime experience of beautiful dinner tables. He surveyed Grandmother's with a critic's eye. "It needs a candle," he said.

He chose a pink one and, with the least possible help, saw that it was properly lighted and placed on the table. "Oh, Grandmother," he proclaimed, "that is bery beautiful."

Bedtime came. A warm, splashy bath was supposedly supervised by Grandfather. Dapper Dan was tucked into bed according to Mike's minute specifications. Grandmother checked off her list of instructions from Mike's mommy: the night-light was on and the door into the blue and antique-white bedroom was partway open. All was quiet.

All was too quiet for Grandmother's ears. Grandmother could hear tears. She went into the bedroom just as the tears became sobs. She gathered her grandchild into her arms. "I want my Mommy!" wailed Mike. All the bravado was gone, all the defenses down.

Grandmother rocked Mike. "I know, I know," she murmured into his wet cheek. "Of course you do."

After a few moments, the sobs subsided. The small form relaxed in Grandmother's comforting arms.

"One time," Grandmother began softly, "when I was about your age, I spent the night at my cousin's house in Tennessee. I had begged and begged my parents to let me stay. Finally they said I could. I had a fun time with my cousins until it was time to go to sleep and all the lights were out. Then I felt so lonesome, I began to cry. I wanted to go home. I cried out loud and woke everybody. I wanted to phone my mother and daddy to come get me and take me home with them. My uncle was very tired and sleepy, and he did not like being waked. He did not like my calling my daddy—who was your great-grandfather—and waking him, either! He took the phone and told my daddy that I was all right. He said, 'Kay just has a little touch of homesickness, and she will be all right in the morning.'

"My mother—your great-grandmother with the red hair—came to the phone and reminded me that I had begged and begged to stay with my cousins. She said that I would have lots of fun playing in the morning. Then she said to me in a very stern voice, 'I think you had better behave yourself, Kay E-LIZ-abeth!' "

Mike had become very still and alert. "Did she really say it that way, 'Kay E-LIZ-abeth!'?"

"Just like that. And when your great-grandmother talked like that, I knew I had better mind her fast."

Mike said the delicious great-grandmother sound again, "Kay-E-LIZ-abeth!" He laughed. He snuggled into the warm bed, smiling.

Grandmother tucked the covers around him. "You are the best boy in this whole town," she said, "and it is so nice to have you here with us." Using the superlative, Grandmother could go no further than the whole town. There was Bill, visiting with his other grandparents in Bryan, and Wesley, up in Kansas City—each equally dear and always a part of any superlative. But Mike heard the intent of her words and was at peace. Grandmother went out of the room, leaving the door open wide.

The Second Day—Saturday

Down the hall, the door to the blue, red, and gold master bedroom had been left open wide too. Very early in the morning, Grandmother heard the soft sound of bare feet in the hall. Part of a small face peered through the door toward the double bed.

Grandmother smiled. With a bound, Dapper Dan and Mike were climbing onto the nearest side of the bed, which happened to be Grandfather's.

Grandfather loved it. When he was really awake, he relished the radiant delight of his small grandson bouncing on the covers above him. He hunched himself up and spilled Mike into the middle of the bed. Grandmother managed a hug and a kiss before she retreated from the gentle roughhousing. Grandfather soon retreated too. Mike reigned supreme on two pillows, surrounded by rumpled sheets and blankets. Dapper Dan, feeling the need of more sleep, was halfway under the covers, snoozing away.

After breakfast, Mike and Grandfather spent part of the morning out in the garage. Mysterious sounds came from the garage, but no amount of questioning from Grandmother produced an explanation. "It's a secret surprise, Grandmother," said a merry-eyed Mike with a glance at Grandfather.

Grandfather backed Mike all the way. "Absolutely," he said.

"But we'll show you when it's finished, won't we, Grand-father," said Mike.

"We'll even bring it inside to let you see it," promised Grandfather. Then he left to do things that needed to be done.

Mike wandered into the living room and made tentative sounds on the keyboard of the ebony grand piano which stood beside a wall of antiqued mirror. Grandmother relished the sounds. The piano teacher part of herself came unbidden and was quickly relegated to a background position. Only as a grandmother would any piano instruction come from this visit.

But Mike's fingers persisting at the keyboard drew Grandmother like a magnet to his side. She showed him how to find Middle C beside the two black keys in the middle of the keyboard. He played it with a stiff forefinger—C, C, C. Grandmother showed him how to curve his fingers as if he were holding an orange in his hand. Mike played Middle C again with a curved forefinger—C, C, C.

"I do believe," said Grandmother, "that you are playing 'Row, Row, Row Your Boat!' "

She played it for him with her curved forefinger and third and fourth fingers: C, C, C, D, E. Mike was amazed as he heard the familiar tune. His forefinger began C, C, C, for "Row, Row, Row." The third and fourth fingers on D, E, barely sounded.

"You did it!" said Grandmother.

Mike tried it again. Grandmother sang softly as he played. The D and E got mixed up. Grandmother, carried away, said, "Try it once more."

Mike sighed. "I'm tired," he said, easing off the piano bench.

Grandmother's heart condemned her for overdoing it. She

glanced at the clock. The complete time at the piano with Mike had taken between three and five minutes. *Even so,* she told herself, *you overdid it. You had to teach instead of just grandmothering.*

She sighed. It was true, and there was no way out for her. Knowing how to teach, it was impossible to "just grandmother," whatever that meant. For her to grandmother was to teach. *But surely I can do it with more of a grandmother finesse,* she yearned, *if I haven't already blown it.*

Mike was out in the backyard. Grandmother waved to him through the kitchen window. He waved back and made a great flying leap out of the swing Grandfather had put on a limb of the peach tree. Grandmother put her hand to her head to show him how amazed she was at such a leap. Mike laughed and did it again.

In the early evening after dinner, Mike and Grandfather and Grandmother watched a TV program which Mike had recommended. The TV was an elderly black and white set which reflected the attitude of the grandparents toward television programming. Mike, down on the carpet in front of the TV, watched and listened intently. Grandfather, with an incredible ability to turn off the external, was reading a theology book. Grandmother, who could not turn off any external sound, was sorting photographs and glancing at the TV. Suddenly Mike saw something that brought his pudgy self to an upright position in front of the TV. "____, but it's beautiful!" he exclaimed.

Grandmother's eyes opened wide. Grandfather glanced her direction. He had heard too. They smiled at the absurdity. While Mike continued to focus on the TV, Grandmother went to Grandfather's chair. "I'm sure it was 'gosh,' " murmured Grandmother, trying not to laugh.

"Of course," chuckled Grandfather. "He certainly wouldn't say anything more than that. And even if he did, I wonder where he could pick up something like that?"

"Don't rule out TV," said Grandmother.

Mike, oblivious to his grandparent's conversation, soon turned off the TV. He had another splashy bath and gladly allowed his tired, pajama-clad self to be put to bed. The newness of his visit had worn off; he had had a busy day. He was tired; he was asleep in minutes.

Mike was sleeping soundly when Grandmother stopped by his bed on her way to her room. She touched his hair, smoothed the covers a bit, and went down the hall to sleep beside Grandfather.

Sometime during the night, a scream split the silence. Grandmother, who had slept by ear since Mike's mommy was born, was at his side in an instant. Grandfather followed, turning on lights.

"There's a dragon in here!" wailed Mike. "A great, big, wormy dragon is trying to get me!"

At this point, Grandfather went back to bed. He knew from long experience that Grandmother was an expert on dragons. He left the hall lights on, doing his part to dispell creatures who love darkness rather than light.

Indeed, the dragon had already vanished, as Mike could see in the lighted room. "It was just a bad dream, Mike," said Grandmother, holding him close. "I used to have bad dreams too, and I would wake up so scared. I would even cry to get in bed with my mother!"

Grandmother paused, and Mike had a moment in which to feel braver. "You were probably younger," he said.

"I hate to tell you, but actually I was even older than you. I was a real scaredy-cat! I kept on having bad dreams and being scared until my mother gave me a meadow."

"What is a meadow?" asked Mike.

"A meadow is a low place between little hills. You can run down the little hills into the soft green grass of the wide meadow. You can fly kites there or play games. If you like, you can just run and run, maybe with a friend or with a dog if you have one. It is a warm, sunny place, and your great-grandmother said that buttercups bloomed there in the spring. In the summertime, there are white daisies, and you can pick all you want for bouquets. Or you can pick the clover from the grass and tie the stems together to make crowns for your head. Oh, it is a beautiful, fun place to be! She told me to think about the meadow if ever I had a bad dream and to remember, 'What time I am afraid, I will put my trust in thee.' "

"That's in the Bible," said Mike. "It means God will take care of us."

Grandmother, feeling quite adequate and secure, grateful for past and present help, tucked Mike under the covers. She gave a last pat, turned off the hall lights, and was almost in the blue, red, and gold bedroom when a wide-awake voice called, "Grandmother!"

She returned to the door of Mike's room. He was sitting bolt upright, obviously fending off a returning dragon.

"Grandmother," said his brave, trembling voice, "what would you do if a big dragon was about to get you— 'Grrrrrrrrrr!' " The growl was terrific and impressive.

Grandmother, who would be the first to give God the glory, replied, "I would call Mike—like this, 'M-I-K-E!'—to come help me and to make him go away."

Mike chuckled. Grandmother heard the bed rock gently as Mike covered himself with the blankets.

The Third Day—Sunday

Grandfather left early, before the rising of the sun. On Sundays, he preached the gospel to some part of creation.

Mike and Grandmother prepared breakfast together, singing psalms, hymns, and spiritual songs in revised or standard versions, according to Mike's needs and specifications. "Happy Sunday morning," they sang, "Happy Sunday morning, We read the Bible, sing and pray, On this happy morning!"

They put on special Sunday clothes with great delight. "You certainly do look pretty, precious," said Mike with the accomplished air of one who often gives a lady pleasure by his approval.

"Well, thank you, sir," said Grandmother. "You look mighty sharp yourself. Do you have a hair brush?"

Mike produced one from his suitcase, and he and Grandmother took turns brushing his hair. Grandmother talked gently and thoroughly to him about "how we act in church." Mike assured her he already knew all that. Grandmother requested a promise from him to do what he knew to do. Mike looked at Grandmother who was looking at him. Mike sighed. "All right, Grandmother," he said.

In the car on the way to church they sang,

> I love God's house, I love God's house,
> And oh, I love his day!
> When Sunday comes, when Sunday comes,
> I cannot stay away!

After the church service, Grandmother smiled at Mike. "Thank you for being so nice," she said, as they drove home in the car. "It was kind of you to help me hold the hymnal."

"It was my pleasure," said Mike. (*His father's good manners*, thought Grandmother.) Then, looking at her from the corner of his eyes, Mike added, "my dear." Grandmother looked at him from the corner of her eyes, and they laughed and laughed and laughed.

It was good to get home and change from their Sunday clothes. Mike, refreshed from napping during most of the worship service, was ready to play in the backyard while Grandmother fixed dinner. Before she had quite finished, Mike ran back into the house. Grandmother thought he had gone to his room, and she was astonished when she heard coming from the piano the unmistakable melody of "Row, Row, Row Your Boat."

Grandmother went noiselessly into the living room. Over and over, Mike's curved fingers (as if he were holding an orange) played the notes. The third and fourth fingers on D and E were firm and secure on "your boat." Grandmother slipped back to the kitchen. When there came a pause in the music, she called, "Mike, that is just beautiful! I love to hear you play."

"Thank you, my dear." The irresistible urge to hear such beauty required his playing it one more time, but it was done in a rush with a break in the rhythm as Mike slid off the piano bench.

When evening came, after Mike was asleep, Grandmother waited for Grandfather's return. She thought of the bright possibility of teaching Mike the next notes for "gently down the stream." She mentally began with the fourth finger

on E for "gent-" and down to the third finger on D for "-ly."
Then the fourth finger on E again for "down," fifth finger on F
for "the," and—oh no! No finger would be left to play
"stream!"

How could she have not thought through the fingering
before she let him learn it the wrong way! Grandmother
sighed. The whole thing was the wrong way, as she well
knew. If he were coming to her for lessons, she would certainly
not begin teaching him this way. She would begin slowly,
gently, firmly, the delightful and exciting venture of inviting a
pupil to learn competence in this difficult and beautiful art.
The way was long—many years long—and to bypass any of
the basic foundation was to ask for a painful relearning experience somewhere along the way.

Mike could not be her pupil, not because he was her
grandson (this fallacy of relationship was laid to rest long ago
by Mozart's father, and more recently by Van Cliburn's
mother) but because he lived too far away, and this circum-
stance was not likely to change. But Mike was only four.
Surely, during these few days, this one small exception to the
rule could be allowed as a diversion during long mornings
alone with Grandmother. She had no doubt of the bliss that
would be Mike's if he should return home as the brilliant
pianist concertising "Row, Row, Row, Your Boat." (Or the
bliss that would be Grandmother's, she sternly required herself
to admit.)

Correcting the wrong fingering would be worth the doing
it would take. It must be done without coercion. Before any
further progress could be made, the incorrect fingering must be
acknowledged, unlearned, and relearned correctly. How in
this world would Mike take to that?

The Fourth Day—Monday

This was going to be quite a day and evening. Grandfather and Grandmother had accepted an invitation to attend the Patrons-of-the-Arts dinner with friends. Arrangements had been made long in advance, and Grandmother had already planned the dress she would wear and the shoes to go with it. She would wash and roll her hair. There was a remote possibility that she might use some mascara at the last minute.

But first things first. Breakfast was bright with reports to Grandfather of what had happened yesterday while he was gone. "I was bery good at church," said Mike, looking at Grandmother for a back-up report.

"I would have to say all day," said Grandmother, as Mike wiggled with delight, now watching for Grandfather's reaction. "It was certainly true at church. All my friends envied my having such a gentleman to escort me."

"Well," said Grandfather, obviously very impressed, "I do appreciate your taking such good care of my girl friend while I was away."

"Your *girl friend*?" Mike was incredulous. "Is Grandmother your girl friend?"

"She certainly is," said Grandfather. "And what's more, I'm taking her out on a date tonight while you go over to stay with Auntie Gin at her apartment. I know it will be hard on you to stay there with her and the three other young women who live there."

"Also two dogs at the last count," sighed Grandmother.

Mike was ecstatic. "When will I go?" he asked.

"We'll take you on our way to the dinner we're going to," said Grandmother. "You'll eat dinner with them. They're having a housewares party tonight."

"What's that?" Mike's eyes were dancing.

"It has something to do with food, so you'll have lots of interesting things to eat," Grandfather told Mike. "But don't forget that you and I have an appointment this afternoon. We're going out for some exploring while Grandmother teaches her piano lessons."

Mike had many things to be happy about. He and Grandfather discussed the necessities for the outing. An appointed time for departure was decided, and Grandmother affirmed that Mike would be ready when Grandfather came. Grandmother and Mike waved as Grandfather departed for his office. They ran back into the house and sat together on the raised hearth in front of the fire to warm their hands.

"Mike," said Grandmother, "I need your help because I have made a mistake."

"You made a mistake, Grandmother?"

"Yes, and I am really sorry about it. I have told you to use the wrong fingers when you play 'Row, Row, Row Your Boat.' I know it will be extra trouble for you, but if you will come to the piano, I will show you the correct fingers to use. It will be a great help to me."

"I will be glad to help you, Grandmother," said the earnest little boy.

They sat at the piano together, and Grandmother explained that instead of beginning with his forefinger, she should have told him to begin with his thumb. "Your thumb is the number one finger for the piano," she said. "And it is the finger to use when you begin 'Row, Row, Row Your Boat' on Middle C." Then she showed him to put his second finger on D for "your" and third finger on E for "boat."

Mike played it grandly. "Oh, Grandmother, that isn't hard. I can do it." He played it again grandly.

Grandmother was truly surprised. "Mike, thank you for helping me on this. I was so anxious to get the fingers in their correct places because now it will be easier to play the next part, 'gently down the stream,' like this." Grandmother played the notes, beginning with the third finger just where it was on E for "gent-", then back down to D with the second finger for "ly," back up to the third finger on E for "down," up to the next note, F, with the fourth finger for "the," and there was the fifth finger ready to play G for "stream!"

Mike made one brave try. Grandmother could tell that neither his fingers nor his heart responded. She gave him a hug as he slid from the piano bench.

The rest of the morning was filled with preparation for the evening. Mike's thoughtful mommy had put things in his suitcases to help celebrate Valentine's Day. There were books of valentines ready to be cut out, pasted, crayoned, mounted, folded—the variations seemed infinite. Grandmother found some packages of lace-paper doilies. Construction paper was also requested and used with creativity. By lunchtime, Mike was ready. There were stacks of valentines for Auntie Gin and the other young women who shared the apartment house. "And these balentines are for the dogs," Mike explained to Grandmother.

The unfinished creations Mike put away in some mysterious place in his room. "You and Grandfather will find out about them on Balentine Day, precious," he said, looking from the corner of his brown eyes.

When nap time came, there was need for reassurances that Mike would be awake for his next adventure. With a pointed forefinger, he admonished Grandmother, "Be sure to wake me up to be ready when Grandfather comes."

"I will have to be sure to do that," said Grandmother, "because both of you have to be gone in time for my piano lessons." With that ring of truth in his ears, Mike napped peacefully.

Almost exactly five minutes after the last piano lesson was finished (Grandfather and Grandmother had synchronized their watches) Mike and Grandfather arrived back home. Grandmother greeted them at the kitchen door.

Grandfather was beaming and saying something about Mike's being a "good Boy Scout." Mike was a dirty bundle of utter joy. His words tumbled over one another as he told about throwing rocks in a creek. He produced two rocks with some kind of varmint still crawling on them. Grandmother barred the way into the house until the rocks and their inhabitants were disposed of.

Mike looked at Grandfather with renewed respect. "You were right," he said.

He and Grandfather found a box in the garage for the precious hoard, and they were then admitted into the house with the understanding that showers were the first priority. Just before the sound of running water covered their conversation, Grandmother heard Mike obviously mimicking words he had heard before, "You just can't understand wimmen," to which Grandfather rejoined, "so it's a good thing they're so pretty," to the sound of smug chuckles.

Grandmother enjoyed such chauvinism. She set to work

making herself as pretty as her limited ability in that field allowed. She was already making progress when a damp, shiny-clean, four-year-old angel submitted to her toweling. She managed some furtive hugs and kisses as he teased her about going out with her "boyfriend."

In another half hour, the three of them were ready to depart for their enchanted evening. Mike had his load of valentines to be generously dispensed to the favored ladies and dogs. Grandfather was resplendent in a dinner jacket. Grandmother wore a long party dress and sparkling earrings.

"You look bery nice, my dear," Mike observed. Grandmother decided it really didn't matter that she had not had time to wash her hair.

The Fifth Day—Tuesday

Breakfast was lively. "All the girls just loved my balentines," Mike reported. "We had brownies for dessert, and I got three!" Grandfather looked envious. "Auntie Gin has a date for tonight." Grandmother listened. "And the dogs tried to eat their balentines!" Grandfather laughed with Mike, and Grandmother refrained from saying she was glad the dogs were chewing on something besides the furniture.

After breakfast, Mike showed Grandmother that he could play quietly, alone in his room. He would have to do this during Grandmother's piano lessons in the afternoon. Grandfather would not be home until later.

Even so, there was a special surprise for Mike this morning. First, he and Grandmother made a short stop at the Woman's Club so that Grandmother could leave a report she was supposed to make at Piano Teacher's Forum, answer roll call, and give her excuse for leaving early. The excuse was obvious as well as bewitching. Enough smiles came Mike's way to make the whole room seem filled with sunshine. Grandmother left wondering if she had gone to bring her report or to show off her adorable grandson. She did not wonder long before coming up with the incriminating answer.

"Now," she told Mike when they were driving away in the car, "we are going where no one else in the whole family has been—not even Auntie Gin or Grandfather! We are going to see beautiful paintings. Some of them are huge, and some are very small. They are in a very new building with fountains all around.

"We will go into the building through a grove of lovely little trees with white bark and red berries. Someday I think their glossy leaves will meet and there will be a roof of branches.

"When we are inside, I will need to hold your hand so we are sure to be together. We can walk and talk as we look. We do not touch things; it is a place to look. Your mommy and daddy will not believe that you have been to the Kimbell Art Museum!"

Mike had been watching the world go by as they drove along, but he heard part of Grandmother's monologue. "Do we have to hold hands all the time?" he asked.

"We'll see," said Grandmother. She parked the car, and they walked by the fountains and through the grove of growing trees. Inside the spacious, quiet museum, Grandmother took Mike's hand. "First, I want you to see the huge paintings by Boucher. They are so beautiful, especially the pink color. And there are lots of little cherubs in the pictures, like the ones on your valentines."

They walked to a large, circular enclosure and stood before the magnificent paintings. Two covered one wall, and on the opposite wall were two more. The grandeur, the opulence, the romanticized beauty which so enchanted second-estate, eighteenth-century France were portrayed in the vibrant, innocent pinks and blues of the paintings. Mike and Grandmother looked at first one wall and then the other. Mike took a deep breath and said distinctly in a clear voice which Grandmother's sensitive ears could not fail to hear, "____, but it's beautiful!"

Grandmother did not even open wide her eyes. She waited a few moments and then she bent her knees and sort of sat on her heels. Her eyes were even with Mike's. "Mike," she said softly, as though this were a confidence between friends, "it is a good thing to say God's name when we are talking to him. Usually, we close our eyes when we talk to God because it is a sacred time for us. Or if we talk to someone about God with our eyes open, we are careful to say his name as though we hallow it. I do not think that was how you were saying God's name just now. I hope you will always be careful to use God's name only when you are talking to him or speaking about him to others."

Mike's answer was just as soft, and just as sincere. "Yes, Grandmother," he whispered.

Grandmother rose and took Mike's willing, small hand. They continued to admire the Bouchers. Grandmother had the distinct impression that what she had said to Mike had been anticipated, that it was not the first time he had heard it, in essence, and that it was a relief to have Grandmother do her duty. Grandmother was never quite sure what really happened. The situation never arose again. Grandmother mentioned it to no one except Grandfather, who thought it of no more consequence than Mike's investigation of other dimensions of God's universe. The thrust of Grandfather's thinking seemed reasonable to Grandmother. She wondered why she felt that because of the incident in the museum she had been given a pearl of great price which neither moth nor rust doth corrupt. Perhaps Grandfather felt the same way about rocks and varmints, but of course, he would never in all this world put it that way.

Grandmother explained to Mike that the paintings were over two hundred years old and that they had been painted in

France. She told him how to pronounce Boucher, and both of them said it several times so they could tell Grandfather and Mommy and Daddy about the French paintings.

They walked to another circular vault to see paintings of children and down the gallery to see a funny painting of a boy running from a not very ferocious-looking bull. Then they walked quite a long way in the other direction to the north court to see the large sculpture of a lady who seemed to float in the air on her side.

Grandmother had forgotten to hold Mike's hand, and she caught up to him as he ran the length of the spacious gallery, just before he encountered a kind and careful security person. Grandmother told Mike it was getting to be lunchtime and they had better go home. Mike gave Grandmother every indication that that was a brilliant idea on her part.

After lunch, while Mike took his nap, Grandmother read the mail. There was a note with many hugs and kisses from Mike's mommy: "We had a beautiful flight to Miami. It is so exciting! Thank you both so much for keeping Mike. It has been excruciating not to call to see how you are faring. It is incredible how much we miss the boys."

That evening, while Grandfather and Grandmother and Mike were at the dinner table, Mike's mommy and daddy did call. A blissful Mike, with sponge-like ability, soaked up their tender love and care. The grandparents were invited to come to the other phone, so Grandmother was listening as Mike described his visit to the Kimbell Museum. "And the Boo-shā's were bery beautiful," he reported. "They were huge clear up to the ceiling and came from France."

Mike was unprepared for the impact of this astounding articulation on his appreciative parents. He was asked to repeat the artist's name, which he did, and shortly thereafter left the phone to the grownups while he went to play. Grand-mother could not resist commenting about the cultural ad-vantages of Fort Worth. The young parents, with warm charm and grace, agreed that the Kimbell was on their own most-want-to-see list and that nothing could please them more than having Mike exposed to it.

Grandfather asked about Bill, and there were glowing reports about his activities with the paternal grandparents. It was a lovely time of communication among three generations.

The loveliness of the evening continued. After Mike's splashy bath, pajama-clad and ready for sleep whenever it came, he stayed up later than usual to watch a special story on television. Grandmother watched it too. Even Grandfather was interested.

Mike sat on the sofa with Grandmother. They laughed together at the funny parts, and sometimes Mike put his head in Grandmother's lap to rest a bit. Grandmother remembered another time and another room. There was no television set, but there were recordings of beautiful symphonic music to lis-ten to. She remembered the times Mike's mother, and her brother and sister, listened to the music as they colored, read a favorite story book, or rested a sweet, sleepy head in her lap.

Grandmother smiled as she remembered. She smoothed the dark hair of her small grandson. It was a lovely evening.

The Sixth Day—Wednesday

On Valentine's Day Mike spent the first part of the morning in his room. Security was tight. He was working on special surprises for dinner. Auntie Gin was going to be there too!

During a break from his labors with scissors and paste, he went to the piano and played "Row, Row, Row, Your Boat" several times. Grandmother complimented him on how well he did it. "And I do wish you could learn 'gently down the stream' because after that comes 'merrily, merrily, merrily, merrily.' "

She sat down at the piano and played the first two lines of the song. Then she lifted her left hand over her right hand and used the forefinger to play the first "merrily" on the C above Middle C! The other three "merrilys" were played with the right hand just where it had been all the time: fifth finger on G for the second "merrily," third finger on E for the third "merrily," and first finger on Middle C for the fourth "merrily."

Mike was intrigued with the first "merrily." He lifted his left hand over his right and tried to find the right note. Fortunately for Grandmother's teaching plan, he missed it. "Show me, Grandmother," said Mike.

"I will, and it will be the most fun of the whole piece," said Grandmother. "But the 'merrily' part comes *after* 'gently down the stream,' and we must do that first."

So, for the joy that was set before him, Mike persevered through the tedious 3-2-3-4-5 fingering of "gently down the stream." It was not easy for him or for Grandmother, but both of them were willing. During the morning, a few minutes at a time, they worked. Just before lunchtime, Mike played the first two lines together without a break in the rhythm, and he smiled at the delight of what he heard. Grandmother rejoiced with him and for him.

While they were eating lunch, Grandfather called to ask if Mike could be ready to go to the zoo for awhile late in the afternoon. Mike could!

There were extra pink candles on the table for Valentine's dinner that evening. The postman had brought valentines from Mike's mommy and daddy, from his dear gram and papa and his brother, Bill, and from his cousin, Wesley. These were put on the table. Mike, with ceremony, brought out his prizes for Grandmother and Grandfather: beautiful, huge "balentines" which they have to this day. Grandfather's was an original creation on construction paper. It had a freehand-drawn heart colored red on a bright green-colored base, over which was pasted a silver lace-paper doily heart. In the middle of the big red heart was pasted a small yellow duck from Mike's cutout book, and it announced, "A Valentine for You." Grandfather loved it.

But Grandmother's was the prettiest of all—just ask her and she will tell you. On an almost square piece of red drawing paper, Mike had pasted the largest and most beautiful valentine from his cutout book. It was a heart of pink and red roses with gold leaves. It was tied with a double red bow. In the middle of the heart were two white doves, one with a rose in his beak, flying toward two winged cherubs, and one with a rose in her hair. The head of this cherub with the rose in her hair was above the heart of roses, and Mike had encircled it with a white lace-paper doily. Another identical doily was under the bottom tip of the heart of roses. Oh, but it was lovely!

Auntie Gin came, laden with valentines. There were valentines from her and from all the women she lived with. The dogs had sent valentines too. Mike liked best the one from Auntie Gin's German shepherd puppy. The table was heaped high with love.

Grandfather said he would like to sing a song for the blessing. Mike began one he had learned in Vacation Bible School. Grandfather, Grandmother, and Auntie Gin sang with him:

> God is so good,
> God is so good,
> God is so good,
> He's so good to me.

They sang it twice with great joy. Auntie Gin said it was one of her most favorite songs in all the world, and everyone thanked Mike for leading them in singing it. "You're bery welcome," said Mike happily.

After Auntie Gin left, Mike and Grandfather cleared the table of valentines, and Grandmother washed the dishes. Mike took his treasure hoard into his room and returned shortly with a cardboard box containing one of his games. "I wish we could play this game," said Mike. "I think you would like it."

The game was opened and spread out on the dining table. It was by and large a game of chance, and try as they would, Grandmother or Grandfather seemed to be in partnership with chance.

Mike did not take lightly to losing the game. He rather vociferously slammed the game back into the box and stalked to his room. "That's not fair!" he cried.

He was called back. "It is very hard to lose a game, Mike," said Grandfather. "But sometimes we lose. All of us do. Even so, it has been fun to play the game, and we ought to tell the other players, 'That was a good game.' Then perhaps they will play with us again sometime, and maybe we will win."

"Well, I'll play you again *right now*," said the angry little warrior, close to tears and speaking rather louder than the acoustics required.

Grandfather and Grandmother said they would be glad to play another game. "But this time, no matter who wins or loses, we will all be good sports and thank each other for playing a good game, OK?"

"OK," said Mike, unfolding the board on the table.

Grandfather and Grandmother were sure Mike would win. They did everything short of openly throwing the game. Let us hope they would not have done that, even if they could. But with a heavy heart, Grandfather found he had won the game.

"I'm never going to play with you again," said the forlorn little boy, as he started for his room.

Grandmother stopped him, put her hands on his shoulders, and said, "Thank you for letting us play your game, Mike." Then gently, firmly, she turned him toward Grandfather. "I think you want to tell Grandfather that it was a good game."

Grandfather looked stricken. "That was a good game," choked Mike.

After a rather solemn going-to-bedtime for Mike, Grandmother came back into the den. "You didn't need to have him say that," said Grandfather. "He has no way of knowing we weren't taking advantage of him."

"I know," said Grandmother, and she sighed. She remembered other nights, when after the happiest of times, things did not go so well with two sweet little girls and their dear brother. Sometimes you lose.

The Seventh Day—Thursday

Dapper Dan came to breakfast the next morning. Grandfather and Grandmother welcomed him with joyous hugs and kisses. "Where have you been, Dapper Dan?" they asked. "We have missed you!"

"He has been bery sleepy and taking long naps," said Mike, obviously pleased with the reception Dapper Dan was receiving. There seemed to be no way for the grandparents to hug Dapper Dan without including Mike in the embrace.

Dapper Dan sat in his own chair at the table and enjoyed breakfast immensely. He waved good-bye to Grandfather as he left for work. Mike and Grandfather had plans for the afternoon.

Grandmother was working with dishes and soap suds when Mike came into the kitchen in a very stern mood. He stood firmly on short, stocky legs, his right hand upturned with a pointed forefinger toward Grandmother. "You promised," he began, and then said more emphatically, "You PROMISED if I learned 'gently down the stream' you would teach me 'merrily, merrily, merrily, merrily,' and you have not kept your promise!"

Grandmother tried very hard to keep her cool. She just managed to change astonishment to horrification. "I can't believe such a thing of myself!" said Grandmother, drying her hands without even rinsing off the soap. Both of them started toward the living room as Grandmother admitted, "I have been very negligent."

Mike was melting at Grandmother's appropriate dismay. She had received almost enough punishment for past and present misdeeds. Almost. "Yes," he said, "you have been bery—." There was a valiant attempt to say "negligent." (Grandmother kept the pronounciation in her heart to warm many a cold day since.) And then Mike added in a generous tone, "my dear."

Grandmother felt secure enough to look down at him out of the corner of her eyes, and Mike chuckled. They went to work on "merrily, merrily, merrily, merrily."

The first "merrily" went beautifully. It was not difficult to locate the next C up from Middle C if the pattern of two black keys was evident. It was evident to Mike right away. His left forefinger went up and over his right hand and played "merrily" many times.

It was not so easy to say "merrily" with the fifth, third, and first fingers of his right hand. The other two fingers kept chiming in unbidden. It took awhile. Even after the "merrilys" began to stay in place, it took some doing to add them to the first two lines of the tune. But after awhile, the three lines began to jell.

Grandmother clapped her hands in approval. "I think we really should let Grandfather hear this," she said. "He just won't believe what you can do." No greater accolade could have been given.

Mike spent the rest of the morning outside in the cold, sunny February day. Grandmother, her eyes and ears tuned to the yard as she did housework, saw him talk to a bright red cardinal perched above him in the live oak tree and found herself wishing to be an artist. She watched him play with imaginary friends. There were other children in the neighborhood, but taking on the involvements and reciprocation of asking them over to play with Mike was the one thing more than Grandmother felt she could do.

Apparently, however, all the thoughts of his imaginary world did not pertain to cardinals. As they ate their sandwiches for lunch, Mike talked of many things. Questions poured from him between bites, preceded often by a factual statement.

"I know about babies," he said. "They grow inside their mothers, and that's why ladies get so big when they are growing babies. Did you get big when you grew babies?"

"Very big," said Grandmother.

"I know how the babies get out, too, but it's bery private to talk about."

"How very true," said Grandmother. "That is a very wise thing to know, and . . ."

"But I don't know how they get in. How do they get in, Grandmother?"

Grandmother had programmed her mental computer concerning "answering children's questions about sex" more than a score of years before. She found herself swiftly pushing imaginary buttons. Everything came up "tell the truth and use correct terminology."

"They get in when the father and mother have sexual intercourse," said Grandmother, "and you are so right about this being very private to talk about—just with Mommy and Daddy and grandmothers . . ."

"And grandfathers," said Mike, taking another bite of sandwich.

Grandmother went into the kitchen for more milk. As she refilled Mike's glass, he said, "Ladies sit down, and boys stand up. Why do ladies sit down and boys stand up?"

Grandmother was conscious of her physical readiness for Mike's nap time, so she suggested to her adored grandson that he discuss that particular question with Grandfather. She never remembered to ask Grandfather about it. There was much hammering out in the garage and many comings and goings between the yard and the garage during the late afternoon.

As soon as dinner was over, the three of them went to the living room. Grandfather and Grandmother sat in chairs to listen. Mike majestically seated himself at the piano and played "Row, Row, Row Your Boat" clean and clear, all the way through "merrily, merrily, merrily, merrily."

Grandfather was properly astounded. He praised Mike as only Grandfather could, and Mike squirmed with pleasure. Then, as only Grandfather could, in complete innocence and sincerity, he said, "I can hardly wait to hear you play the rest of it!"

Grandmother, with no innocence at all, took advantage of such psychological help. "Let's do it now, Mike," she offered, coming toward the piano.

"I'm too tired," said Mike, edging off the piano bench.

Grandmother was oblivious to her poor timing in reaping the impact of Grandfather's remark. "Oh, come on, Mike. All we have left to do is 'life is but a dream,' and that won't be very hard at all." She tried to sit down beside him.

"I don't *want* to!" wailed Mike.

"Some other time, maybe," said Grandfather.

Grandmother yielded, with the sickening realization that she had done it again. Mike went to his room, and Grandfather had things to do in the den. Grandmother, walking toward the kitchen, asked herself why she could not do what she knew to do. *Repeat after me,* she mentally ordered, *I am his grandmother, period. But oh dear,* she thought, *time is running out. Tomorrow is Friday, and he probably won't want to do it yet. And Saturday may be too late to really get it put together.*

Mike came into the den holding a now-familiar cardboard box. "Grandfather, I wish you would play this game with me, and you, too, Grandmother, will you play with me?"

Grandfather, caught in a situation he thought would not recur, looked for a way of escape. "Isn't there a television program you want to see, Mike? Grandfather has some things he needs to do." Grandmother gave him a withering glance.

"Just one game, Grandfather? I will be a good sport." There was no denying that request.

The three of them sat at the table, and chance soon had Grandmother far behind in the competition. She prayed that Grandfather would not win. With a heart full of love for Grandfather, she prayed it. It was a neck and neck race, but finally it looked as if Grandfather had won.

Mike was now familiar with the rules. "I have one more turn because I began after you did, Grandfather," he reminded.

"That's right, Mike," said Grandfather with renewed hope.

Mike took his turn. He did not win, but with a small smile, he sighed and announced, "We tied, Grandfather. That was a good game. That was a good game with you, too, Grandmother."

Grandfather came alive. "That was really a good game, Mike. You had me scared there, and you almost beat me!"

Even in a culture where winning is everything, Mike seemed to feel a bit of exhilaration at the playing of the game.

His smile expanded, he tucked his box under his arm and started for his room. He stopped at the den door, looked at them with twinkling eyes, and said, "I know how to play now."

Grandfather and Grandmother tried to believe their small hill of joyous harvest. Sometimes you win.

The Eighth Day—Friday

They woke to rain the next morning. Before they could finish breakfast, the rain had turned to sleet. Grandfather, with Mike's able assistance, set logs to blazing in the fireplace. Grandfather left for work, inching the car cautiously down the street. During the morning, the bare limbs of the peach tree began to glaze over as the world outside turned to ice.

"Why do we have winter?" asked Mike.

Grandmother's eyes sparkled in anticipation of what that question could bring. "Have you ever heard of a place where it was always winter and never Christmas?" She went to the bookshelves and drew out a small volume from the well-worn set of books by C. S. Lewis.

"Never Christmas?" Mike was incredulous. "Oh, it's a book! I think my mommy told me about it one time. Will you read it, Grandmother?"

"I would love to," said Grandmother. They sat side by side on the sofa in front of the warm fire, and for a blissful quarter-hour, they went to the land of Narnia. The journey was a bit complicated for a four-year-old, but Grandmother knew the way so well that she could tell it by heart as they looked at the pictures.

Grandmother would have spent the morning there; but as soon as the White Witch was disposed of, Mike was back to earth again and ready for new adventure. "You remember, Grandmother,"—there was that pointed forefinger again, so she should have been prepared—"you remember you were going to teach me the rest of 'Row, Row, Row, Your Boat.' "

Grandmother sped down Lantern Waste past the Lamp Post and through the Wardrobe and found herself beside Mike at the piano. "Life is but a dream" went well. Grandmother's corrected fingering paid off. The fifth finger stayed put to begin "life" on G, the fourth finger played F for "is," the third finger was ready for "but" on E, the second was an easy D for "a," and there was the thumb in place for "dream" on Middle C! Mission accomplished!

Well, almost accomplished. The reentry of "Row, Row, Row," and the playing of the whole tune at one time proved traumatic. First one line and then another became unglued. But Grandmother was pretty sure it would come together. She now had the one more day she had hoped for. And there was Grandfather's availability as an audience in the evening.

For an icy-day treat, Mike and Grandmother had lunch in front of the fire, and they watched Mike's favorite cartoon program on TV together. When it was finished, they turned off the TV and had fun dunking cookies in their glasses of milk. "Just this once," said Grandmother, "because of all the ice."

They laughed together, then with no warning whatsoever, Mike asked, "Grandmother, will you tell me about hell?"

Grandmother's computer sent out sparks as it revved again and came up with the same answer, "tell the truth as best you know it and don't hesitate to admit what you don't know."

"We believe, from our study of the Bible," said Grandmother, "that hell is a place for the devil and his followers."

"I don't want to go there," said Mike.

"No one *has* to go there," said Grandmother. "Do you remember John 3:16? 'For God so loved the world, that he gave his only Son, that whoever believes in him should not perish but have eternal life.' " They said it together, Grandmother quite evenly, and Mike stumbling through the words he had almost memorized.

"Is God real?" asked Mike.

"God is *really* real," said Grandmother.

"I guess it's time for my nap," said Mike.

Grandmother smiled and agreed. Nap time was warm and snuggly. Dapper Dan needed an extra blanket because of the ice. They slept and woke and waited for Grandfather, who came home earlier than usual, driving slowly and carefully on the icy street.

Mike and Grandmother lost no time announcing to Grandfather that a concert was about to begin. Grandfather, saying he could hardly wait to hear it, sat in a chair in the living room while Mike wriggled onto the piano bench. Grandmother sat near the piano. It was well she did because Mike's fingers needed a little encouragement a couple of times. Even so, the whole tune came through, and Grandfather applauded with enthusiasm. Mike and Grandmother clapped too.

Then, as only he could, in innocence and sincerity, Grandfather asked, "Aren't you going to let him announce his piece and do the bowing like you have your piano pupils do at recitals?"

"Of course," said Grandmother, "that's the very next thing!"

With Grandfather looking on approvingly, Grandmother taught Mike how to bow from his hips, his back and legs straight, arms and hands relaxed. "You do this when you first

come to the piano and just before you announce your piece,"
explained Grandmother. "When you have finished playing,
you bow again."

They practiced the whole procedure from scratch. The
three of them sat in chairs, and Grandfather said, "Mike,
would you please play for us?"

"I would be glad to," said Mike (as any polite pianist
would, according to Grandmother), rising and going toward
the piano.

Grandmother and Grandfather applauded. Mike turned,
bowed, and announced, "I shall play 'Row, Row, Row, Your
Boat.' "

He sat at the piano, played with few mistakes his master-
piece, slipped carefully off the bench, and bowed again to great
applause from his audience. Only the proverbial duckling taking to water can be compared to Mike's taking to bowing,
announcing, and applause. "A real ham," said Grandfather
later, "just like . . ." He paused, laughing as Grandmother
raised her eyebrows and squinted her eyes at him, "just like the
rest of the family!"

Grandfather and Mike could do little work out in the cold.
But they made several trips to get logs for the fire, and it blazed
in merry reds and blues and yellows to warm the spirit as well
as the body. Grandmother gratefully acknowledged their ef-
forts and told them no one could do it so well as they. "Nat-
urally!" Mike and Grandfather congratulated each other.

Grandmother began boiling herbs and spices to prepare a
court bouillon for shrimp. Grandfather and Mike were drawn
to the delicious smell, and Grandfather got a stool for Mike so
that he could see everything. Grandmother began saying, "Be
careful, be careful." Mike and Grandfather said they were

helping, and they laughed and were so happy to be helping.

Mike began to sing at the top of his voice, "God is so good! God is so . . ."

"Mike!" Grandmother said sharply with frowning severity. "I have told you we do not play about God!"

The mood in the kitchen changed instantly. Mike, still standing on the stool, said in a husky whisper, "I wasn't playing, Grandmother." He began to get down from the stool.

A stricken grandmother realized she had been mistaken. She reached for Mike, and he waited while she told him, "Oh, Mike, I'm sorry! I thought you were trying to be funny and playing, but I see you were not. I'm really glad you feel that way."

"That's all right, Grandmother," he said in the same soft, husky whisper. He went toward his room. Grandfather had already gone out the door to the garage.

Grandmother wept in the kitchen. She reminded herself that Mike had had no playmates for a week, that he had brought nothing but joy to her even though he missed his mommy and daddy and brother. *What an inadequate substitute-parent I make for him*, she told herself. *I am not even an adequate grandmother*.

Grandfather came in, opened a drawer where tissues were kept, and handed several to her. "I hope you're not crying in the shrimp," he said, with the audacity born of lengthy experience. "And I do hope you can live with the fact that you are not completely perfect all the time."

"I am *not* crying," sniffed Grandmother right on cue, just as Grandfather had anticipated. The timer buzzed, and Grandmother poured the steaming pan of pink shrimp into a colander to drain. "And you don't have to remind me I'm not perfect, but I just wish I wouldn't be so far from it with a sweet, darlin' little boy," her voice broke into a sob.

Grandfather took Grandmother into his arms, and at first her body was held stiffly away from his. After all, he had told her she wasn't perfect. But at his gentle pats and loving words, she softened close to him. It was a time-worn ritual that served them well. In minutes, Grandmother was melting butter for the sauce, and Grandfather started toward Mike's room.

"Don't you tell him that I cried," admonished Grandmother.

Whatever Grandfather said to Mike, the two of them were beaming when they came to the dinner table for plates of pink shrimp on a bed of rice, covered with a creamy yellow cheese sauce. As the three of them sat at the table together, the world righted itself.

After dinner, out came the game again. This time, there was never any doubt about the outcome. Mike won, hands down.

"I won!" His joy was almost more than they could bear. They congratulated him, told him it had been a good game, and meant every word of it.

"And you won it fair and square," said Grandmother. "I was trying to win too!"

"I'm going to have to concentrate more," said Grandfather. "I can't let this keep happening!"

"I will play you again tomorrow night," said Mike, folding his game into the box. He added, with a chuckle, "That was a bery good game."

The Ninth Day—Saturday

Rain came with the morning. The ice melted into it, and there was promise of better weather the next day. But today was rather on the dreary side. Mike was in no hurry to dress, and Grandmother and Grandfather finally told him to take his time and come in whenever he liked. They sat at the breakfast table, and Grandfather returned thanks. As he ended the blessing, a loud "Amen" came from Mike's room. He bounded in, took his place at the table, and the day was not so dreary after all.

Grandfather promised to be home early in the afternoon to finish the surprise he and Mike were working on. Mike's eyes sparkled with anticipation. "I can hardly wait to see it," said Grandmother.

"I'm looking forward to hearing 'Row, Row, Row, Your Boat' again," said Grandfather.

Mike and Grandmother waved to Grandfather as he left, then they pulled the garage door down quickly to keep out the rain. As they stepped through the door and into the kitchen, Mike asked, "What had we better do first, Grandmother?"

"Well," said Grandmother, "we need to get your things ready to pack for the trip home tomorrow."

"But first, I think we should practice 'Row, Row, Row, Your Boat,' don't you, Grandmother?"

"Oh, I certainly do," said Grandmother, making an easy, quick decision.

They worked together for five minutes, maybe seven. *There is no way,* Grandmother reminded herself, *a piano teacher could do this.*

Mike watched TV while Grandmother worked in the kitchen. Then they practiced again, and in no uncertain terms, "Row, Row, Row, Your Boat" came together. Mike knew the way the tune should sound, so his ear guided him. Rhythm was a part of him. The steady beat of something he had previously learned to sing flowed out in perfect measure. It was, for a four-year-old, quite a feat.

The time to pack had come. Mike's suitcases were brought out of the closet and opened. Their emptiness soon vanished and a little bit more. "Of course, we must leave out the things you will need tonight and in the morning," said Grandmother. "But we can pack everything else. Now let's see if we've forgotten anything."

Mike was not saying very much as they packed. He brought a pack of paper and crayons to the suitcases. "Here are my balentine things," he said.

"Thank you, Mike," said Grandmother. "And oh! We don't want to forget Dapper Dan! Where is he?"

Mike said nothing. Grandmother looked around the room for Dapper Dan. Under the wide, curved dresser, beneath one of the middle drawers, Grandmother thought she saw Dapper Dan's foot sticking out. Of course, she couldn't be sure. She glanced at Mike, and she saw that he was looking toward the dresser. "Maybe he will turn up later," said Grandmother.

"I think he's hiding," said Mike. "He doesn't like to pack."

"Not that we would pack him!" said Grandmother. "He likes to make a trip in the car, so I feel sure he will be ready in the morning. This is all the packing we need to do for now, anyhow. How about some lunch?"

They had a fun lunch, then it was nap time, and soon after that, Grandfather came home. There was a concert in the living room, and Mike gave a flawless performance of his repertoire, complete with a brilliant announcement of the title, and dignified bowing from the hips. There was tremendous applause, and Grandfather said he could hardly believe his ears at such perfection. "I can hardly wait for you to play it for your mommy and daddy and Bill tomorrow."

Mike and Grandfather spent most of the afternoon in and out of the garage. Grandmother could hear sawing, hammering, banging, laughter, silences, and the murmur of conversation. The rain stopped, and more than once bright sunshine between the breaking clouds lit up the backyard. It was almost dinner time when Grandfather and Mike made a triumphful appearance in the kitchen. Mike had his hands behind him, and now it was Grandmother's time to be surprised and impressed.

Grandmother found her part very easy to play. Her astonishment was genuine as Mike held out, in both hands, a little wooden boat. "Oh!" said Grandmother, "that is just beautiful! I don't see how you ever did it!"

"I did it by my bery own self," said Mike, "and Grandfather helped me."

"Well, said Grandmother, "I knew you were making something, but I never dreamed it would be as nice as this!" She touched the boat, admired its smooth sides, and asked many questions. Explanations were gladly given and would have been even more lengthy had not the timer announced that things in the oven were ready for dinner.

The pink candle was lit by Mike and Grandfather. The

boat became a part of the centerpiece, particularly on the side most visible to Mike. They sat at their places, Mike on the big dictionary, Grandfather at the head of the table, and Grandmother at his right.

"I would like us to have a song for our thanks tonight if you will lead us, Mike" said Grandfather.

"I will be glad to, Grandfather," said Mike, glancing at Grandmother.

"Thank you, Mike," said Grandmother.

Mike began the song and led them as they sang it twice, once joyously forte, and the second time almost pianissimo:

> God is so good,
> God is so good,
> God is so good,
> He's so good to me.

Grandmother furtively wiped her eyes on her napkin before the last line was completed. All of them were smiling as they began to eat their given bread.

"I think we had better call your mommy and daddy," said Grandmother as they cleared the table. "They were so nice to ask us to come to Sunday dinner, but there are things I must do at Sunday School in my department. However," there was a special tone in Grandmother's voice, and Mike looked at her in anticipation, "since it would be good to get there as soon as we can, I am fixing some sandwiches. We will eat lunch in the car on the way if Grandfather has no objections."

Grandfather, who had arranged his Sunday plans to go with them, had no objections, as Grandmother was fairly sure. "That is a great idea," said Grandfather. "Those sandwiches in the car taste so good!"

Mike had no objections, either, but his mind was on other

matters. "Before we call them," he got right to the point, "I would like bery much to play my game with you." His eyes were merry.

"Oh-ho!" said Grandfather, "you think you are going to beat me again! Not on your life!"

Grandmother laughed. "This time, I am going to have to beat you both," she said.

Much to her surprise, it looked as if she would do just that. But when the game ended, the grandparents, their joy complete, congratulated the small, adorable, chubby victor. He seemed to grow in wisdom and stature before their eyes. "You can call Mom and Dad now," he said huskily, "I think they want to know when we are coming."

Grandmother hastened to do her duty. The happy young parents were soon on the line, listening to their little boy tell them he had won the game—again. "It was a bery good game," he acknowledged, every inch a gentleman.

After the grandparents talked a minute to their oldest grandson, they completed plans for the next day with his parents. Mike was soon asleep. Grandfather, after closing the garage for the night, reported that the sky was full of stars.

The Tenth Day—Sunday

Dapper Dan had reappeared and was sitting on top of one of the suitcases when Grandmother came into Mike's room to check last-minute packing. "He's ready to go," said Mike, who was tugging at sheets and bedspread, getting his chores finished. "Is the lunch packed in the car?"

"It will be when we're ready to go to church. And we'll leave your play clothes out so you can change to them in the car because we won't be coming back by here before we go," said Grandmother.

The schedule went smoothly. Shortly after noon, Mike and Grandmother and Grandfather were having their picnic in the car. The sandwiches were devoured, along with crunchy things. "I should have put in some fruit," sighed Grandmother. "How could I have forgotten to put in fruit!"

Mike and Grandfather told Grandmother it didn't matter at all, but Grandmother kept on wishing she had put in fruit. There was a thermos of water and a smaller one of coffee. There was gum for everyone, and everyone kept the inside wrappers to use for depositing used gum. Until it was needed, Mike made his into a little boat. He put the wrapper boat into the smooth wooden boat he had made with Grandfather. Something on the inside of the wrapper sparkled when the sun found it. Mike held the boat so the sun made glory all around.

"Look, Grandmother! Diamonds!"

"Oh, Mike, how beautiful!" said Grandmother. Grand-father thought it was beautiful, too, but he could only glance at it while he was driving.

In less than two hours, Mike was home again, and there was joyful reunion with many hugs and kisses. The young parents clasped their child, and Mike took on renewal in their arms. There was no doubt he had come home again.

The grandparents opened their arms to their beloved seven-year-old grandson and received his wholehearted, loving response. The three of them talked, and Bill became part of a surprise to come.

They sat in the living room and visited and ate delicious things prepared by Mike's mommy. The smooth, wooden boat was brought from the car, and Grandfather and Mike reveled in congratulations and admiration. When there finally came a moment's lull in the lively conversation, Grandmother caught Bill's watchful eyes, looked toward the piano, and nodded her head.

Bill's voice was impressively casual and serious. "Mike," he said, "would you play something for us on the piano?"

The young parents, momentarily surprised, caught the feeling of something planned. They waited expectantly. Mike, hearing his cue from an unexpected voice, nevertheless re-sponded as the seasoned, polished artist he was. "I would be glad to," he said, rising and going toward the piano.

The grandparents and Bill applauded, and the young parents joined in immediately. Mike turned to them, bowed from the hips, and announced, "I shall play, 'Row, Row, Row, Your Boat.' "

He played it flawlessly, his stocky legs dangling over the piano bench, the bare patch of his tummy almost covered by his T-shirt. His left forefinger rose as if on wings over his right hand to do the first "merrily." There was never a more convincing rendition of "life is but a dream."

He slipped off the piano bench and bowed again to tremendous and prolonged applause which came sincerely and unrehearsed from his audience. True to her genes, his mother furtively wiped away a tear as she and his amazed father exclaimed and asked a multitude of questions about how this had come about. Grandmother, who had expected this moment to be a pretty good one, was almost overwhelmed at finding it exceeded anything she could have asked or thought.

Mike was constrained to give several encores, which he did generously, never skimping a bow. His audience remained enthusiastic, but Grandfather and Bill began munching refreshments again. Mike and his father soon joined them, and the two ladies went to another part of the house to check on Mike's suitcases.

It was soon time for the grandparents to start their trip home, and there were many hugs along with the good-byes. "When are we going to Grandmother and Grandfather's house again?" said Mike, and everyone laughed and teased him.

"Maybe in about three weeks," said his mommy and grandmother almost together. There were waves and kisses from the grandparents in the car and from the beautiful, reunited family, who stood in the yard, watching the car out of sight.

As the car sped over the miles of smooth, wide, freeway, there was a deep, relaxed silence between Grandfather and Grandmother. The relaxation came not from relief, except for the physical kind, which does not spring from the heart. It was more an emotional relaxation, not from trial, which they had

sometimes borne together, but from the awesome wonder of
seeing dreams come true, of experiencing evidence that what
they had prayed for had been agreed to by God, and presented
as a gift to open now. That they could not see the whole, they
knew; that in a moment of time, everything could be changed,
they often reminded themselves; but they had been given the
loveliness of today's gifts, and their gratitude was great.

Grandmother sat near the middle of the front seat, close
to Grandfather, her hand resting lightly on his knee. If she had
moved more than slightly in the other direction, Grandfather
would have said, "What is the matter?"

She put her head down on his shoulder, and he moved a
bit, trying to make it more comfortable for her to do so. He
leaned his head down to hers for a moment's touch. "Hello,"
he said.

She sighed in contentment. "I've missed you."

"I'm glad to hear it," he said smiling, as he watched the
smooth road ahead.

They talked together then, in words that were their own
particular language of endearment and understanding. It was
a relationship enriched and complicated by parenthood and
grandparenthood and one that could burst into argument and
even anger without an instant of warning. But it was one that
had found stability in the acceptance of "for better, for worse,
for richer, for poorer"—a man-woman thing, by mercy and
grace made in the image of God.

On the way home, they went by a favorite antique place.
They stopped, mostly for the joy of being able to stop if they
wanted to. They examined and admired the lovely, old pieces
that had once belonged to someone else, but they were too tired
to make decisions. So they returned to the car and very shortly
arrived home.

They walked into the house and found they were not prepared for what they thought they had prepared themselves for. The pink candle was on the table. The big dictionary was slightly askew on Mike's chair. Mike's chair. As they walked past the bath off the hall, Mike's little stool was in place so that he could reach the soap to wash his hands. *Ah,* thought Grandmother, *Saint-Exupéry's fox was prepared to remember* le petit prince *when he saw the sun on the wheat, but did he discover that remembrance lived in everything the sun shone on?*

When they came back to the den, Grandfather picked up the big dictionary to put it away, and Grandmother said, "I'll take the pink candle . . ." Her voice broke, and there was no hiding tears from Grandfather.

"Oh, come on now," he said, "you're not going to act that way, are you?"

"Of course not," she said, and she meant it. She put the candle on the shelf and went into Mike's room to pull the drapes for the night. The well-made (for a four-year-old) lumpy bed put lumps in her throat, so she threw back the spread and took off the sheets and deposited them in the bathroom clothes hamper. The little stool had been put away, and Grandfather was reading in the den.

She made herself remember how happy she was. She went to the kitchen and began to put things together for a snack. She hummed a little tune that kept running through her head. Too late she realized it was coming out, "God is so good, God is so good."

"That's not fair," said Grandfather, his voice breaking.

They looked at each other and smiled with understanding. There was no way around it or over it. Something had happened in the house these past ten days. Mike was here.

Afterward

Grandmother was sleeping. Or was she? Something was in the dark room. She strained her eyes and ears. Then she saw it. A huge, horrible, wormy dragon was in the corner of the room. It began to come toward her with a mighty, "Grrrrrrrrr!" Oh, she was so scared!

But Grandmother knew what to do. She called, "Mike!" Then louder, "M-I-K-E!!"

He came, leaping and running toward the dragon. How tall and bright he was! With what rich gifts he was arrayed! He wore a helmet of salvation, his armor gleamed with righteousness, and in his hand was a shining sword of faith!

At the mere sight of him, the dragon vanished. Grandmother looked at where it had been, and it was just not there. She looked in all the corners. It was gone.

She turned to look at Mike. He was still running and leaping and just as bright, but the brightness seemed to come from warm sunshine in a clear blue sky. Was he farther away? Or was it that he was not so tall? Why, of course, he was only four years old, running on firm stocky legs, his feet in worn tennis shoes, his tummy rounded above the elastic of his short pants.

There was no sword in his hand. It was a kite, and he was letting it fly higher and higher, as he ran in a beautiful meadow filled with buttercups and daisies. She could barely see, following at his heels, a small copper-colored dog.

She recognized her mother's meadow, and she was not at all surprised to find Mike playing there. She felt she must let him know how much she appreciated his disposing of the dragon, so she called, "Thank you, Mike!"

He saw her, waved, and seemed to understand just what she was trying to tell him. But he was deeply involved with his kite, and he only took time to say with a chuckle, "You're bery welcome, my dear."

Grandmother longed to go to him, but she knew he needed to keep running with the kite. She turned and found she was turning toward soundly sleeping Grandfather in their double bed in the blue and red and gold bedroom.

Almost soundly sleeping Grandfather. His arms went out to her and drew her close to his side. As she snuggled her head on his shoulder, Grandmother whispered softly in his ear that she had been dreaming.

Only Grandmother, whose ears were tuned to Grandfather's noiseless sounds, could have heard him murmur, "Life is but a dream."